Relaxing Coloring Book

Geometric Lines

5310
publishing
.com

50
PACK!

5310 Publishing Company

5310publishing.com

ISBN: 978-1-990158-04-9

First edition (this edition) released in January 2021.

Designed by Alex & Eric Williams

Help us fight world hunger! Go to NotebooksForLife.com to learn more.

For every minute you are angry you lose

sixty seconds of happiness.

- Ralph Waldo Emerson

Happiness is not something you postpone for the future; it is something you design for the present.

- Jim Rohn

If more of us valued food and cheer and song above hoarded gold, it would be a merrier world.

- J.R.R. Tolkien

Let us be grateful to the people who make us happy; they are the charming gardeners who make our souls blossom.

- Marcel Proust

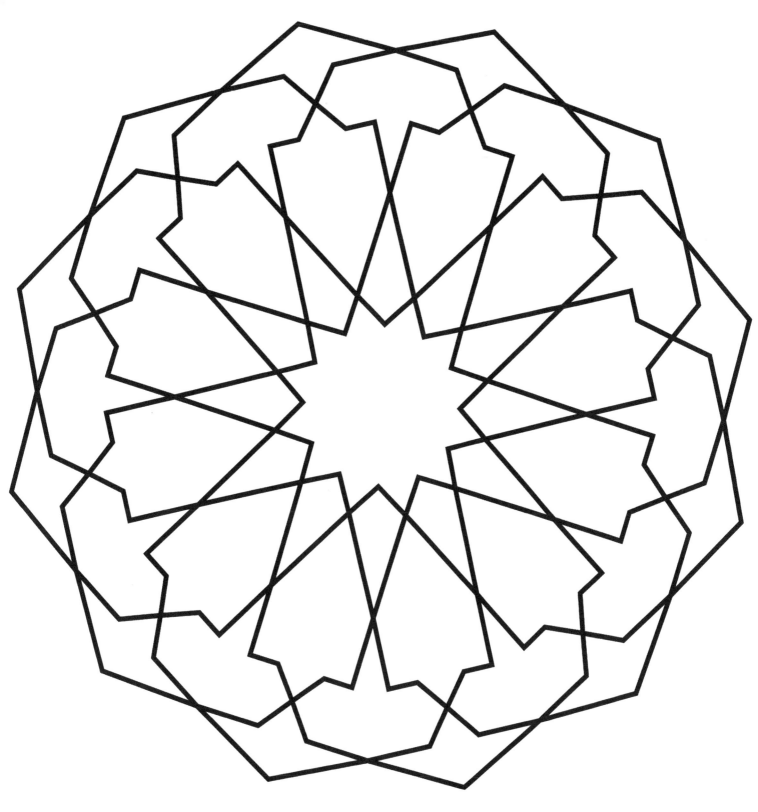

Learn to value yourself, which means:

fight for your happiness.

- Ayn Rand

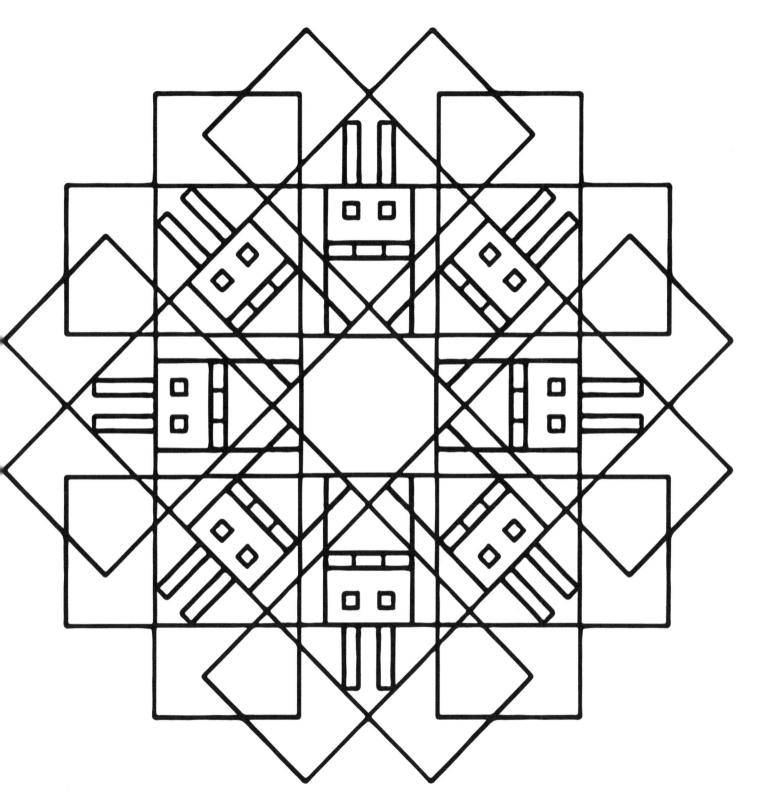

The happiness of your life depends upon the quality of your thoughts.

- Marcus Aurelius

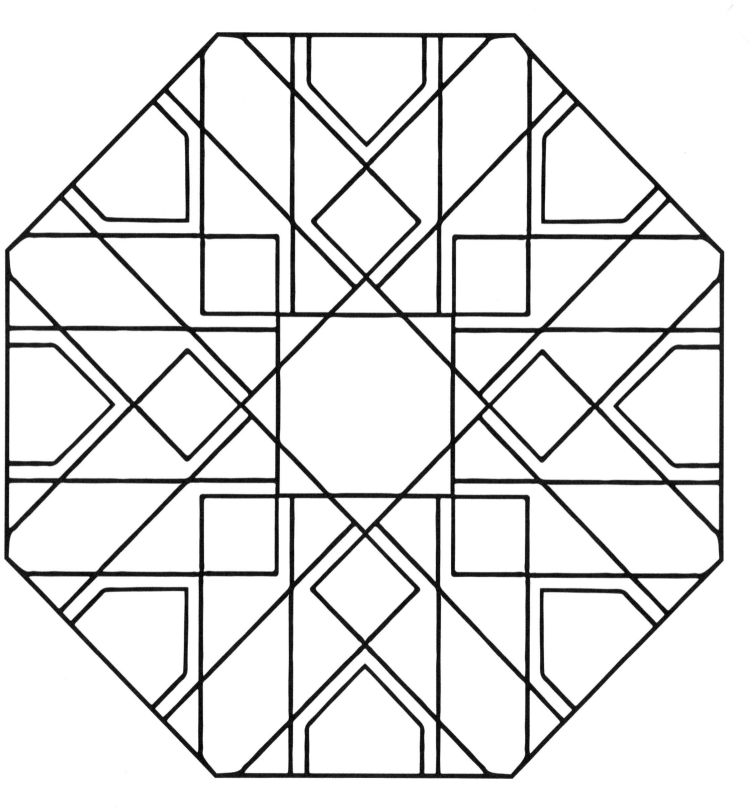

The best way to cheer yourself up is to cheer someone else up.

- Mark Twain

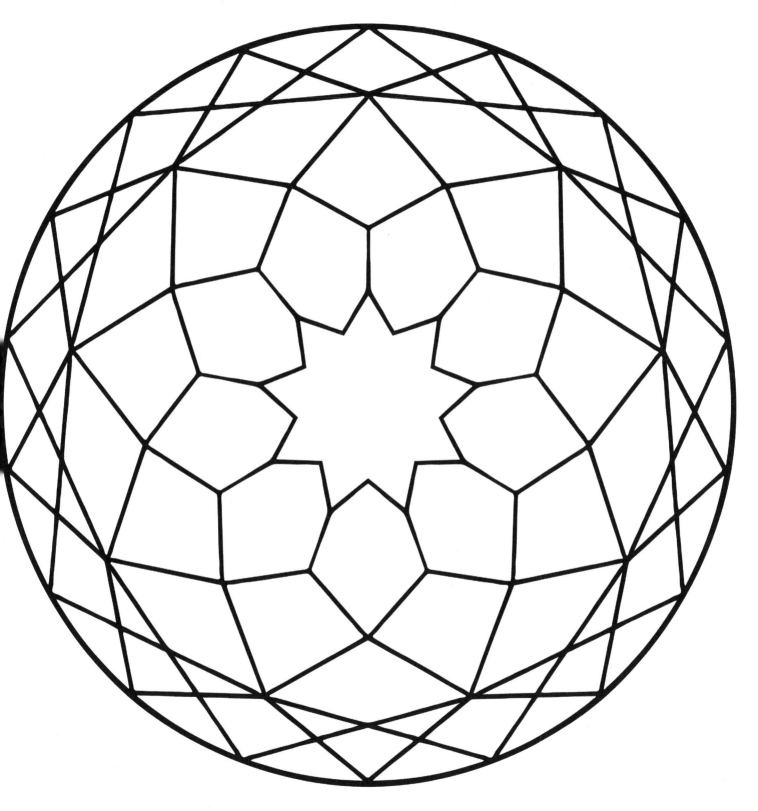

The advantage of a bad memory is that one enjoys several times the same good things for the first time.

- Fredrich Nietzsche

Happiness depends upon ourselves.

- Aristotle

Those who are looking for happiness are the most likely to find it, because those who are searching forget that the surest way to be happy is to seek happiness for others.

- Martin Luther King Jr.

Happiness is not a goal...

it's a by-product of a life well lived.

- Eleanor Roosevelt

Action may not always bring happiness, but there is no happiness without action.

- William James

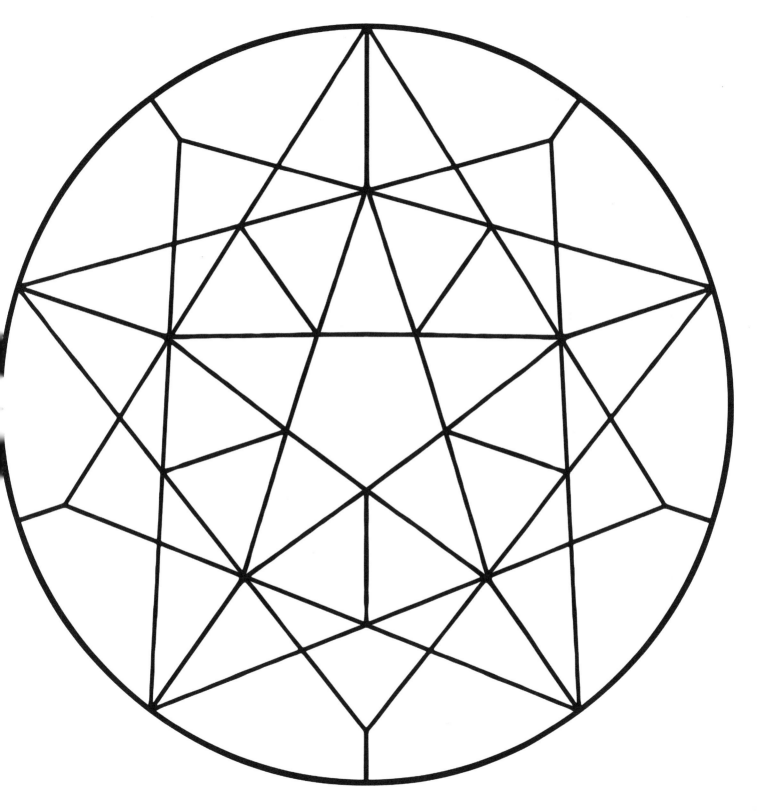

The greater part of our happiness or misery depends upon our dispositions, not upon our circumstances.

- Martha Washington

The successful man will profit from his mistakes and try again in a different way.

- Dale Carnegie

Be yourself; everyone else is already taken.

- Oscar Wilde

It's never too late to be what you might have been.

- George Eliot

When one door of happiness closes, another opens; but often we look song long at the closed door that we do not see the one which has been opened for us.

- Helen Keller

Whatever you are, be a good one.

- Abraham Lincoln

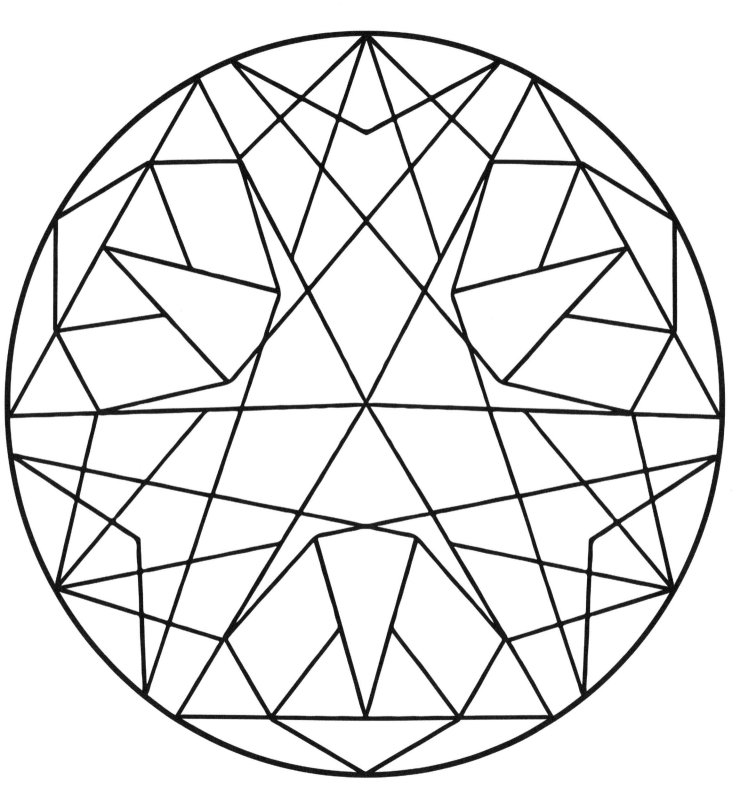

Isn't it nice to think that tomorrow is a new day with no mistakes in it yet?

- L.M. Montgomery

Fantasy is hardly an escape from reality. It's a way of understanding it.

-Lloyd Alexander

Love is the absence of judgement.

- Dalai Lama XIV

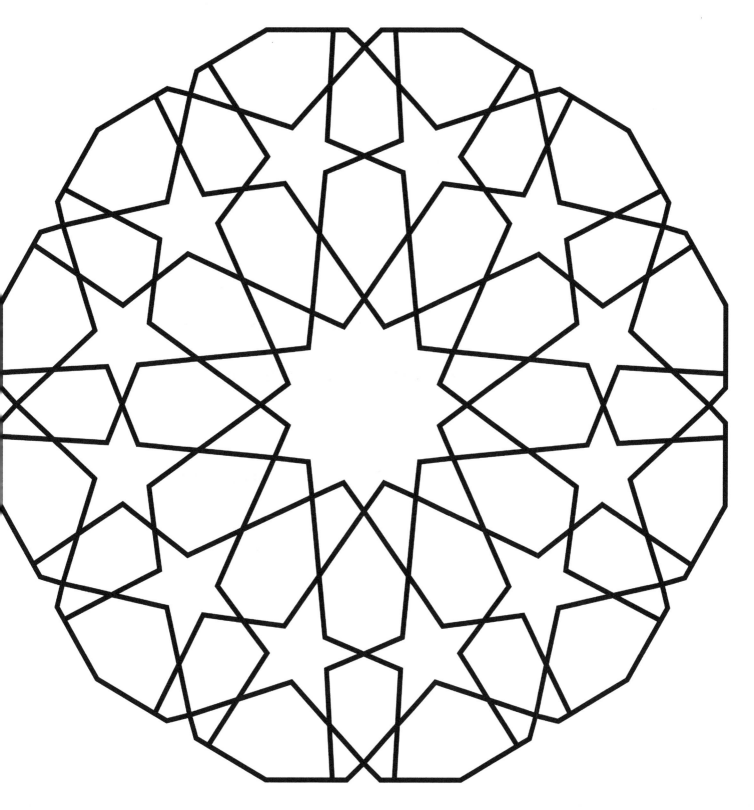

When you're at the end of your
rope, tie a knot and hold on.

- Theodore Roosevelt

Keep away from people who try to belittle your ambitions. Small people always do that, but the really great make you feel that you, too, can become great.

- Mark Twain

Everyone thinks of changing the world, but no one thinks of changing himself.

- Leo Tolstoy

Never doubt that a small group of thoughtful,

committed, citizens can change the world.

Indeed, it is the only thing that ever has.

- Margaret Mead

Peace begins with a smile.

- Mother Teresa

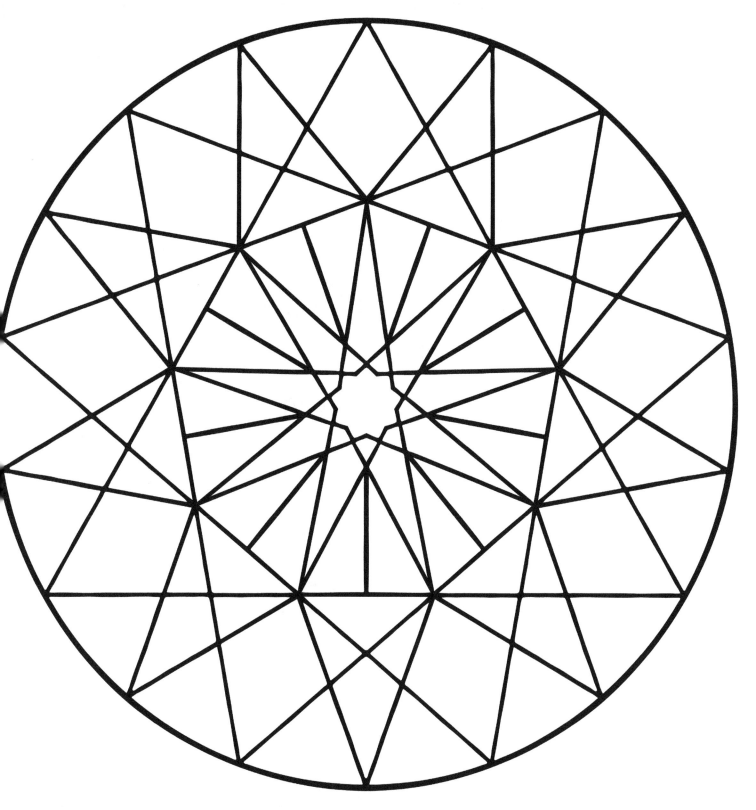

Your task is not to sell love, but merely to seek and find all the barriers within yourself that you have built against it.

- Rumi

Always do what you are afraid to do.

- Ralph Waldo Emerson

Make it a rule never to give a child a book

you would not read yourself.

- George Bernard Shaw

Quality is pride of workmanship.

- W. Edwards Deming

In a time of deceit, telling the truth is a revolutionary act.

- George Orwell

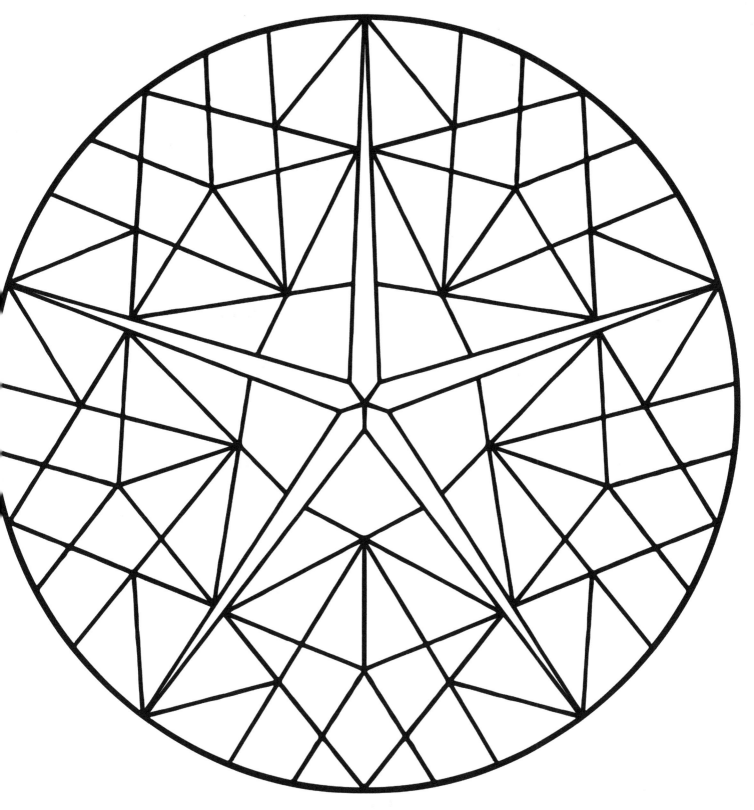

Think of all the beauty still left

around you and be happy.

- Anne Frank

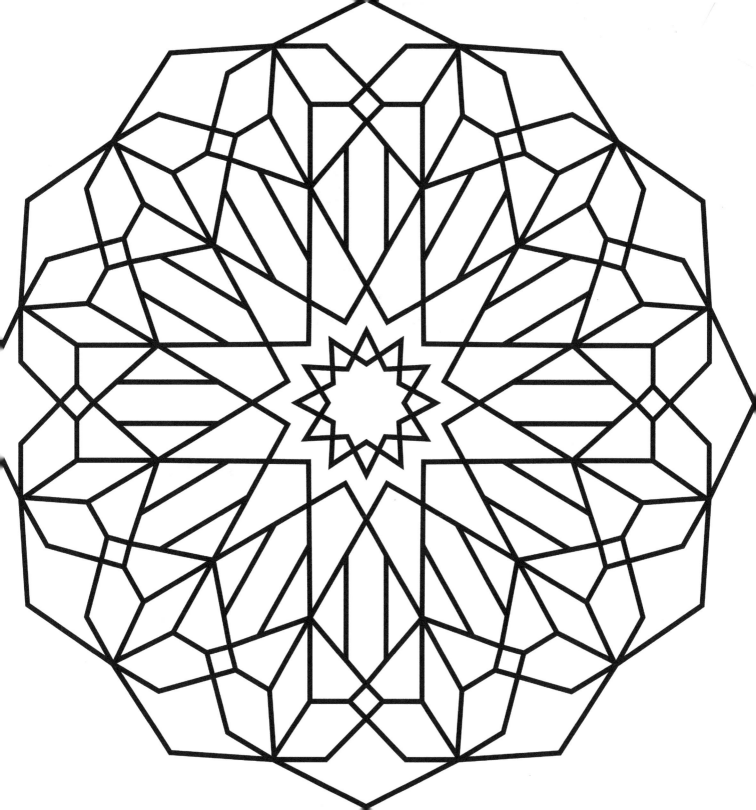

A thing is not necessarily true

because a man dies for it.

- Oscar Wilde

Do not go where the path may lead, go instead where there is no path and leave a trail.

- Ralph Waldo Emerson

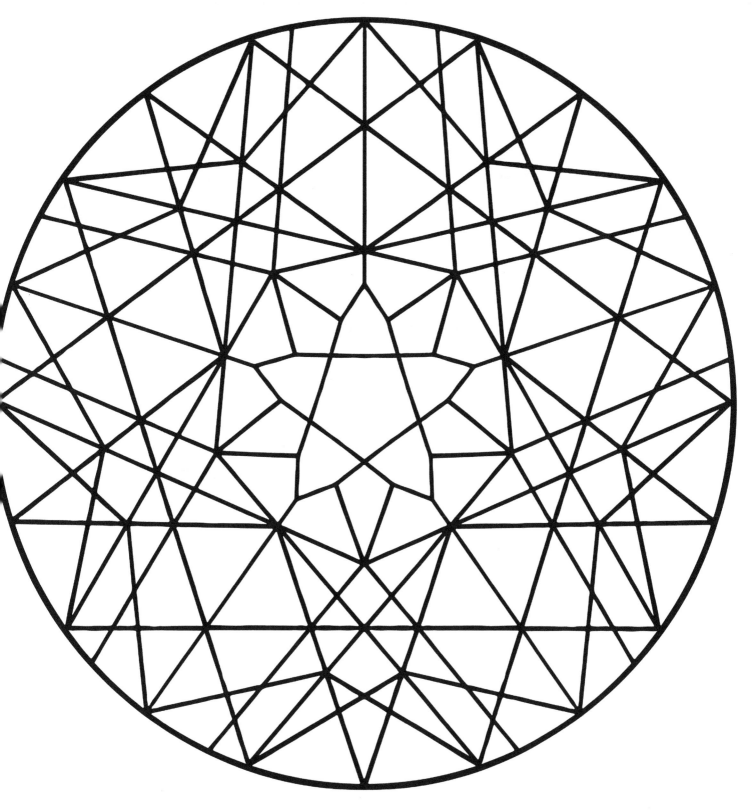

Either write something worth reading or

do something worth writing.

- Benjamin Franklin

Turn your wounds into wisdom.

- Oprah Winfrey

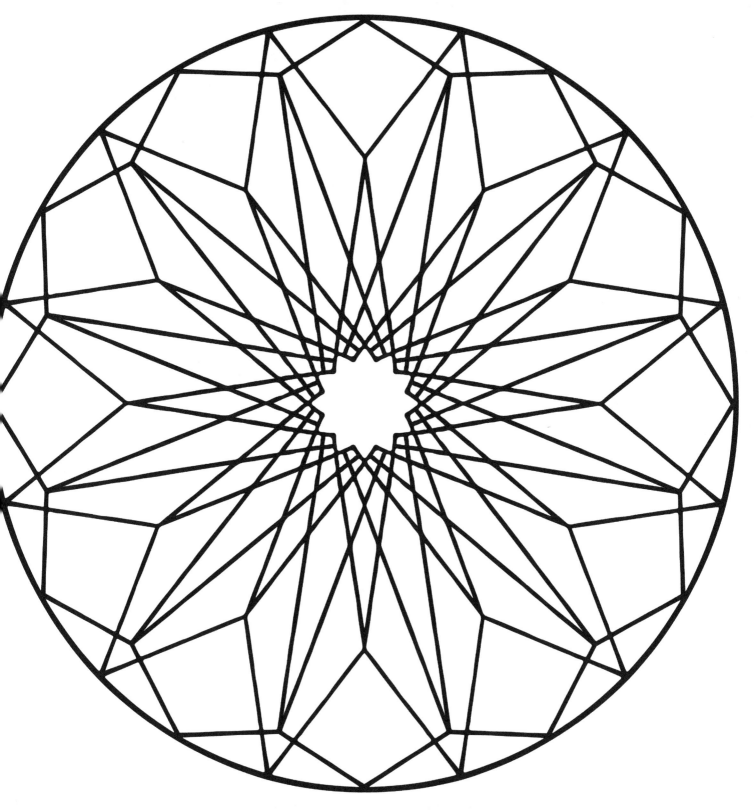

Wise men speak because they have something to say; fools because they have to say something.

- Plato

Why in fit when you were born to stand out?

- Dr. Seuss

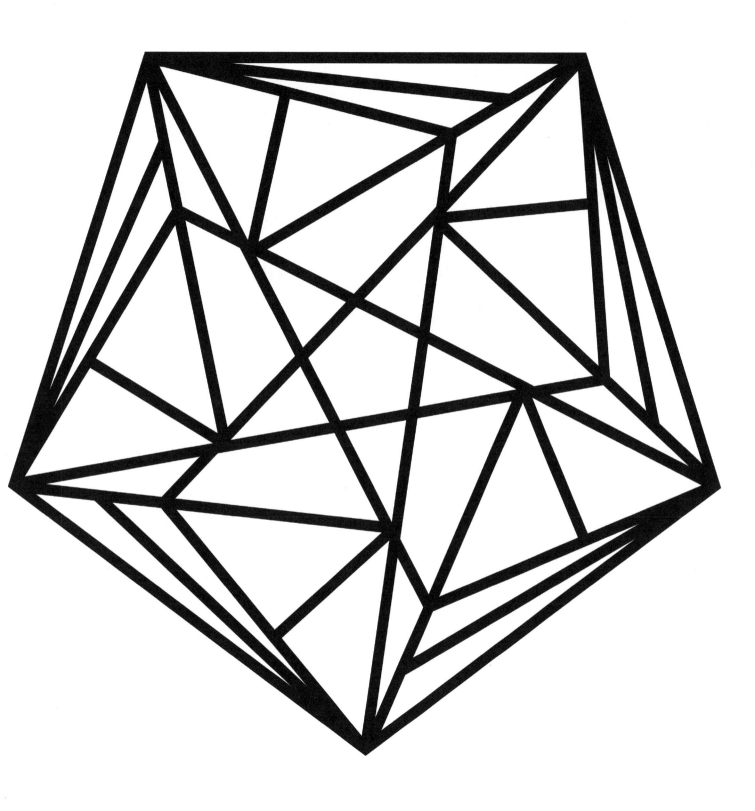

Never be afraid to raise your voice for honesty and truth and compassion against injustice and lying and greed. If people all over the world would do this, it would change the earth.

- William Faulkner

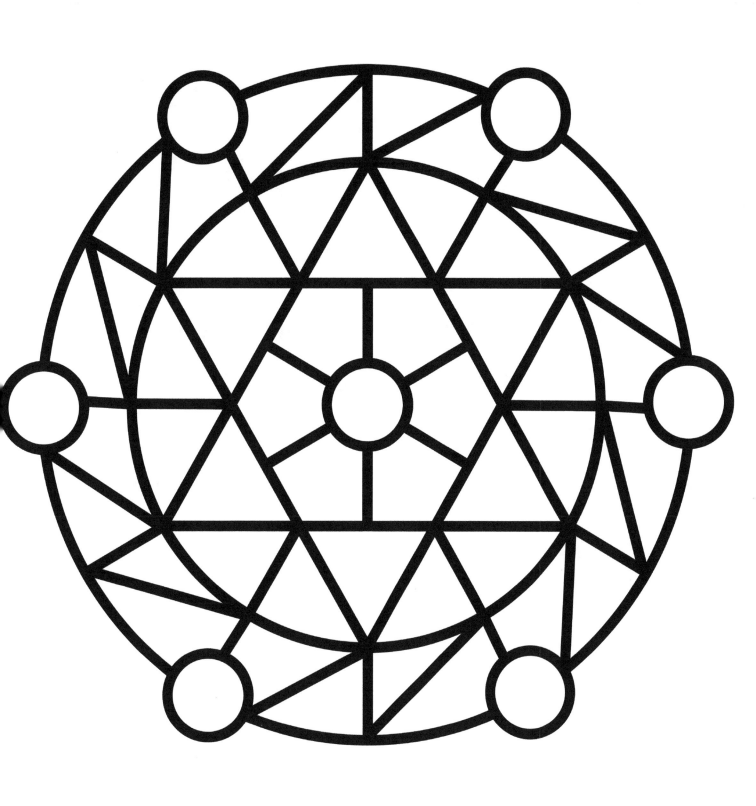

If you have a garden and a library, you
have everything you need.

- Cicero

It's not denial. I'm just selective
about the reality I accept.

- Bill Watterson

Don't judge each day by the harvest you
reap but by the seeds that you plant.

- Robert Louis Stevenson

But I know, somehow, that only when it is
dark enough can you see the stars.

- Martin Luther King Jr.

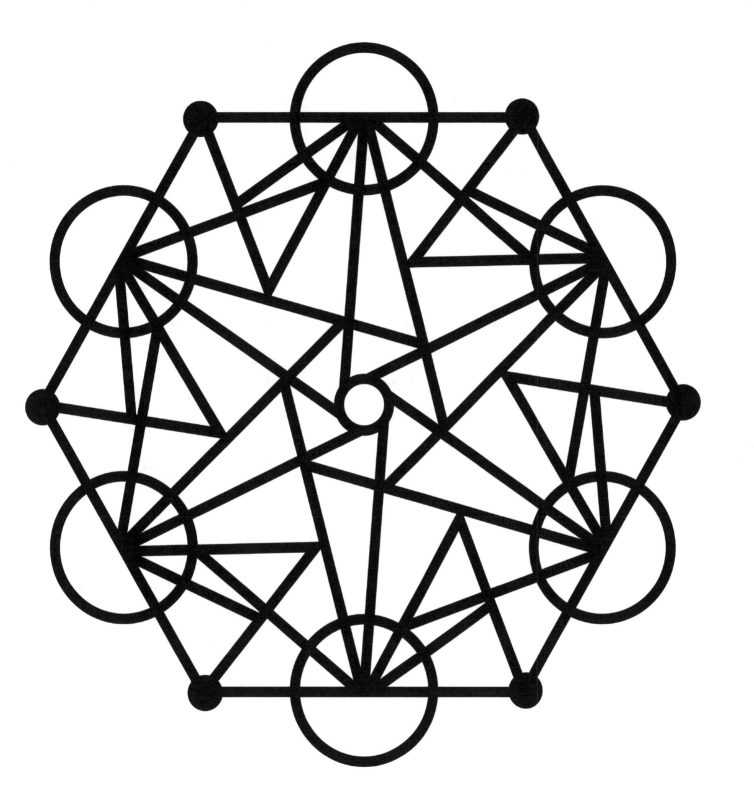

Blessed is he who expects nothing, for he
shall never be disappointed.

- Alexander Pope

Sometimes our light goes out, but is

blown again into instant flame by an

encounter with another human being.

- Albert Schweitzer

It is better to fail in originality than

to succeed in imitation.

-Herman Melville

Lack of direction, not lack of time, is the problem. We all have twenty-four hour days.

- Zig Ziglar

The only way of discovering the limits

of the possible is to venture a little

way past them into the impossible.

- Arthur C. Clarke

Do not fear to be eccentric in opinion, for every opinion now accepted was once eccentric.

- Bertrand Russell

Somewhere, something incredible

is waiting to be known.

- Carl Sagan

It's kind of fun to do the impossible.

- Walt Disney

Test your markers for bleed-through on this page

Test your markers for bleed-through on this page

〇 _____   〇 _____

〇 _____   〇 _____

〇 _____   〇 _____

〇 _____   〇 _____

〇 _____   〇 _____

〇 _____   〇 _____

〇 _____   〇 _____

〇 _____   〇 _____

〇 _____   〇 _____

〇 _____   〇 _____

〇 _____   〇 _____

Test your markers for bleed-through on this page

Test your markers for bleed-through on this page

Bonus Mandalas!

For more adult colouring books go to

5310publishing.com/mandalas

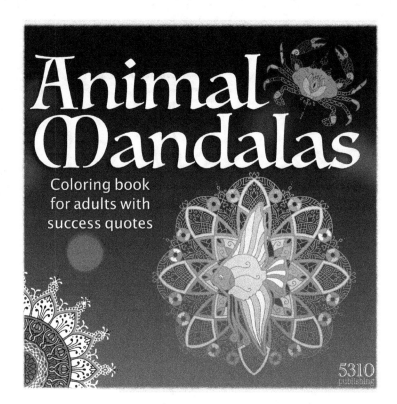

Point your phone's camera at this page to learn more about "Animal Mandalas"

ALWAYS BEAR IN MIND THAT YOUR OWN
RESOLUTION TO SUCCEED IS MORE
IMPORTANT THAN ANY OTHER.

-ABRAHAM LINCOLN

Full-page Mandalas

Coloring book for adults with success quotes

Point your phone's camera at
this page to learn more about
"Full-page Mandalas"

For more adult colouring books: 5310publishing.com/mandalas

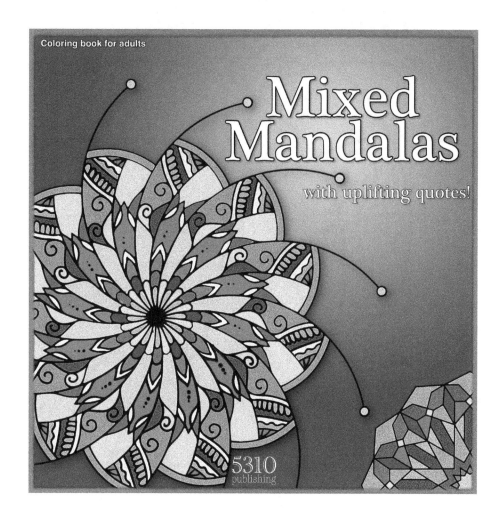

Point your phone's camera at this page to learn more about "Mixed Mandalas with uplifting quotes!"

Point your phone's camera at
this page to learn more about
"Zen Mandalas"

Point your phone's camera at this page to learn more about "Detailed Mandalas"

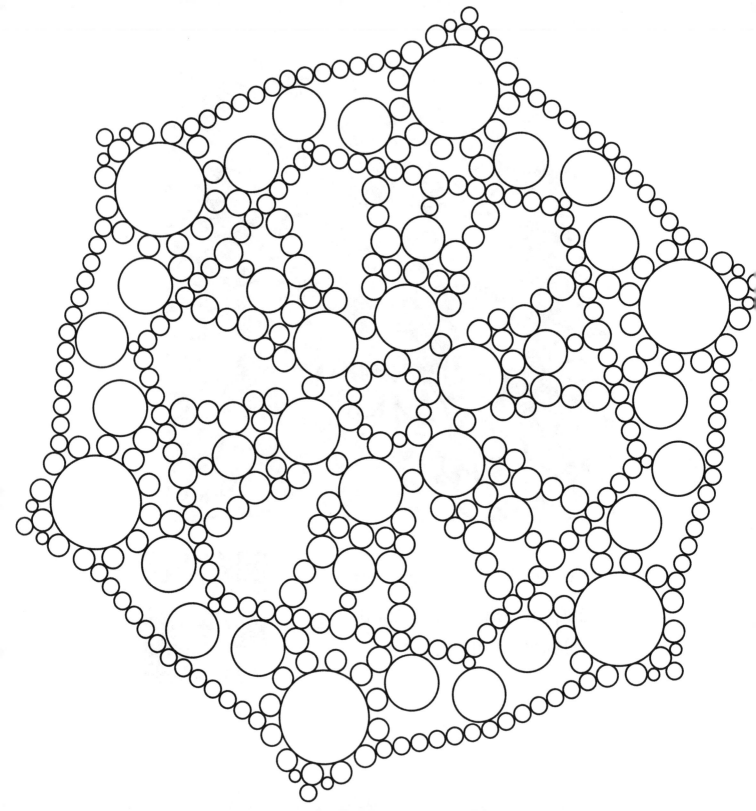

Point your phone's camera at
this page to learn more about
"Mandalas for Any Mood"

Are you a writer?
Do you have good stories to tell?
Publish with us!

Go to 5310publishing.com to become
a published author!

Help us fight world hunger!
Go to NotebooksForLife.com to learn more.

Printed in the USA
CPSIA information can be obtained
at www.ICGtesting.com
LVHW082145010424
776128LV00038B/1254